RICHARD RODGERS
OSCAR HAMMERSTEIN 2nd

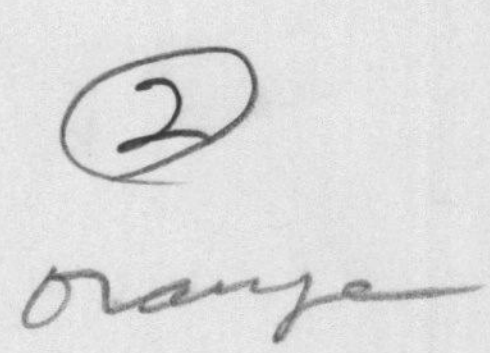

Carousel

WILLIAMSON MUSIC, INC.
609 Fifth Avenue • New York 17, N. Y.

THE THEATRE GUILD

presents

CAROUSEL

A Musical Play

based on

FERENC MOLNAR'S

"LILIOM"

As adapted by BENJAMIN F. GLASER

Music by

RICHARD RODGERS

Book and lyrics by

OSCAR HAMMERSTEIN, 2nd

Production directed by ROUBEN MAMOULIAN

Production under the supervision of
Theresa Helburn and Lawrence Langner

Musical Director
JOSEPH LITTAU

Costumes by
MILES WHITE

Settings by
JO MIELZINER

Dances by AGNES DE MILLE

VOCAL SCORE

(Edited by DR. ALBERT SIRMAY)

Price, $9.00

First performance at the Majestic Theatre, New York
April 19, 1945

CAROUSEL

Cast of Characters

CARRIE PIPPERIDGE	JEAN DARLING
JULIE JORDAN	JAN CLAYTON
MRS. MULLIN	JEAN CASTO
BILLY BIGELOW	JOHN RAITT
BESSIE	MIMI STRONGIN
JESSIE	JIMSIE SOMERS
JUGGLER	LEW FOLDES
1ST POLICEMAN	ROBERT BYRN
DAVID BASCOMBE	FRANKLYN FOX
NETTIE FOWLER	CHRISTINE JOHNSON
JUNE GIRL	PEARL LANG
ENOCH SNOW	ERIC MATTSON
JIGGER CRAIGIN	MURVYN VYE
HANNAH	ANNABELLE LYON
BOATSWAIN	PETER BIRCH
ARMINY	CONNIE BAXTER
PENNY	MARILYN MERKT
JENNIE	JOAN KEENAN
VIRGINIA	GINNA MOISE
SUSAN	SUZANNE TAFEL
JONATHAN	RICHARD H. GORDON
2ND POLICEMAN	LARRY EVERS
CAPTAIN	BLAKE RITTER
1ST HEAVENLY FRIEND (Brother Joshua)	JAY VELIE
STARKEEPER	RUSSELL COLLINS
LOUISE	BAMBI LINN
CARNIVAL BOY	ROBERT PAGENT
ENOCH SNOW, JR.	RALPH LINN
PRINCIPAL	LESTER FREEDMAN
DOCTOR SELDON	RUSSELL COLLINS

Synopsis of Scenes

TIME: 1873-1888

PRELUDE

An Amusement Park on the New England Coast. May.

ACT I

SCENE 1. A tree-lined path along the shore. A few minutes later.

SCENE 2. Nettie Fowler's Spa on the ocean front. June.

ACT II

SCENE 1. On an island accross the bay. That night.

SCENE 2. Mainland waterfront. An hour later.

SCENE 3. Up there.

SCENE 4. Down here. On a beach. Fifteen years later.

SCENE 5. Outside Julia's cottage.

SCENE 6. Outside a schoolhouse. Same day.

TABLE OF CONTENTS

ACT I

ACT II

Prologue
(The Carousel Waltz)

No. 1

Richard Rodgers

cresc.
Allegro moderato
p dolce

Ped.
Ped.
Ped.
Ped.
mf
8
f
8
mf cresc.
poco a poco

cresc.
ff
f
mf dolce
Ped.
dim.
rall.
pp
r. h.

Con spirito
f
8
stacc. sempre

stacc. sempre
ff
Meno mosso
p

Un poco lento, ben cantabile
mf
f

ff
ben sost.
p rit.
l.h.
Ped.
sim.
r.h.
Leggiero
mf

f
mf

ff
f
8
8
f
8

p subito
accel. e cresc.
poco a poco
8
ff marcatissimo

ff

mf *rit.* *sf* *a tempo* *mf* *sf* *mf* *f* *sf* *ff*

Più mosso
mf
f
cresc.
poco
a
poco
8
ff
8
Presto
mf
cresc.
al
fine
sff
gliss
8

Change of Scene

No. 2

Opening Act I Scene II

No. 3

Allegro vivace
Curtain. Carrie and Julie enter.
Piano
mf staccato
Repeat until Mrs. Mullen enter

Mister Snow

(Julie and Carrie Sequence)

No. 4

ue: **Billy**: ...."Keep your money, I'll pay"

Billy exits after Mrs. Mullin, Carrie taps Julie's shoulder.

Lyrics by
scar Hammerstein 2nd

Music by
Richard Rodgers

queer one, Jul-ie Jor-dan! You are qui-et-er and deep-er than a well, And you
Julie:
Carrie:
nev-er tell me noth-in'! There's noth-in' that I keer t' choose t' tell! You been
act-in' most pe-cul-iar! Ev-'ry morn-in' you're a-wake a-head of
Julie:
me, Alw-'ys set-tin' by the win-der. I like to watch the riv-er meet the

Allegro moderato
Carrie:
sea.
When we work in the mill,
pp leggiero
weav-in' at the loom, Y' gaze ab-sent-mind-ed at the roof, And
half the time yer shut-tle gets twist-ed in the threads 'Till y' can't tell the
Julie:
Carrie:
warp from the woof. 'Tain't so! You're a
mf

Moderato
queer one, Jul-ie Jor-dan! You won't ev-er tell a bod-y what you think. You're as
Julie: (speaks)
tight-lipped as an oyst-er, And as si-lent as an old Sa-hai-ra Spink! Spinx!
Slowly
Carrie: Huh? Julie: Spinx. Carrie: Uh-uh. Spink. Julie: Y' spell it with an "x". Carrie: That's only when there's more than one.
pp legato
Julie: Oh! Carrie: Julie, I been bustin' t' tell you somethin' lately. Julie: Y' hev? Carrie: Reason I didn't ker to tell you
before was 'cause you didn't have a feller of yer own.
Now y' got one, I ken tell y' about mine.
Julie: "I'm glad you got a feller, Carrie." What's his name?

Moderato con grazia
Carrie: (sings)
His name is Mis - ter Snow, And an up - stand - in' man is
p
l.h.
l.h.
sim.
he. He comes home ev - 'ry night in his round - bot - tomed boat With a
net full of her - ring from the sea. An
mf
p
al - most per - fect beau, As re - fined as a girl could

wish, But he spends so much time in his round - bot - tomed boat, That he
can't seem to lose the smell of fish!
mf
The fust time he kissed me, the whiff of his clo'es Knocked me
flat on the floor of the room, But now that I love him, my

heart's in my nose, And fish is my fav-'rite per-fume! Last
night he spoke quite low, And a fair spok-en man is
he, And he said, "Miss Pipp-er-idge, I'd like it fine If
I could be wed with a wife, And, in-deed, Miss Pipp-er-idge, if
p

rall.
you'll be mine, I'll be yours fer the rest of my life!" Next
rall.
mo - ment we were prom - ised! And now my mind's in a
maze, Fer all it ken do is look for - ward to That
cresc.
won - der - ful day of days.
f

REFRAIN
Moderato (with expression)
When I marry Mister Snow,
p dolce
The flowers 'll be buzzin' with the hum of bees, The
birds 'll make a racket in the church-yard trees, When I
marry Mister Snow.
mf

Then it's off to home we'll go, And
both of us 'll look a lit-tle dream - y - eyed, A - driv - in' to a cot-tage by the
o - cean side Where the salt - y breez - es blow.
He'll car - ry me 'cross the thres - hold, And I'll be as meek as a
p
mf

lamb. Then he'll set me on my feet And I'll say, kind a sweet,
"Well, Mis - ter Snow,_ here I am!" Then I'll
mf
p
kiss him so he'll know That
ev - 'ry - thin' 'll be as right as right ken be, A -

liv - in' in a cot - tage by the sea with me, For I
mf
love that Mis - ter Snow, That young, sea - far - in',
mp
bold and dar - in', Big, be - whis - kered, o - ver bear - in'
poco a poco cresc.
dar - lin', Mis - ter Snow!
f rit.
rall.
f

Scene Billy and Julie
(If I Loved You)

No. 5

Cue: Billy: Say, tell me somethin', ain't you scared of me?

Un poco più mosso
stay.
You could-n't take my mon-ey If I did-n't hev an-y And I
mf
mp leggiero
don't hev a pen-ny, that's true! And if I did hev mon-ey, You
could-n't take an-y 'Cause you'd ask and I'd give it to you!
Billy:
You're a
Meno mosso
queer-one Ju-lie Jor-dan, Have y' ev-er had a fel-ler you give
p

Julie: (spoken)
Billy: (sings)
mon - ey to? No! Ain't 'y ev- er had a fel- ler at all? No! Well 'y
must - a had a fel - ler you went walk - in' with? Yes! Where'd you
walk? No-where spec-ial I re - call In the
woods? No! On the beach? No! Did you love him? No, never loved no one, I told you that.
Billy: (speaks)
You're a funny kid.
rit.
pp
ppp

Molto sostenuto
Billy: Want to go into town and dance maybe? Or--
Julie: No, I hev to be keerful!
Billy: Of what?
Julie: My character. Y'see I'm never goin' to marry.
(sings)
I'm
pp allarg.
mp
Tempo I. (Allegretto)
nev - er goin' to mar - ry. If I was goin to mar - ry I
would - n't hev 't be sech a stick - ler. But I'm nev - er goin' to mar - ry, And a
girl who don't mar - ry Hes got to be much more per - tick - ler!
p

Billy: Suppose I was to say to you that I'd marry you?
Lento
Julie: You?
Billy: That scares
pp legato
you, don't it? You're thinkin' what the cop said.
Julie: No, I don't pay any mind to what he said.
Billy: But you wouldn't marry anyone like me, would you?
Julie: Yes, I would if I loved you, it wouldn't make no difference what you did, not even if I died fer it.
Billy: Ah... how do you know what you'd do if you loved me? Or how you'd feel or anythin'?
Julie: I dunno now how I know.
Billy: Ah—

Allegretto moderato
Julie: Jest the same I know how I
....how it'd be.... If I loved you.
Julie: (sing
When I
worked in the mill Weav - in' at the loom, I'd
gaze ab - sent - mind - ed at the roof. and
p delicato
legato sempre

half the time the shut - tle 'd tan - gle in the threads, And the
warp - 'd get mixed with the woof If I
Billy: (speaks) But you don't!
Julie: (speaks) No I don't.
Julie: (sings)
loved you But
Broadly
some - how I ken see jest ex - ack' - ly how I'd be.
rall.
pp
rall.

If I Loved You

Moderato espressivo
p a tempo
If I loved you, Time and a-gain I would try to say
p
a tempo
All I'd want you to know
If I loved you, Words would-n't come in an eas - y way.
Round in cir - cles I'd go!
cresc.

Long - in' to tell you, but a - fraid and shy,
mf
I'd let my gold - en chan - ces pass me by!
Soon you'd leave me Off you would go in the mist of day,
p
Nev - er, nev - er to know
cresc.

How I loved you If I loved you!
mf molto espr.
f
mp
Ped.
(They sit in silence, he studies her for a moment, then turns away)
L'istesso tempo
pp
Billy: Well, anyway. .You don't love me. That's what you said, wasn't it?
Julie: Yes.
(Some blossoms drift down to their feet. Billy picks one up and smells it.)
sempre pp
Julie: I can smell them, can you?
The blossoms.
pp
The wind brings them down.

Moderato con moto
Billy: (speaks ad lib.) Ain't much wind tonight. Hardly any.
Billy: (sings)
pp
Ped.
✲ simile
You can't hear a sound, not the turn of a leaf, Nor the fall of a wave, hit-tin' the sand. The tide's creep-in' up on the beach like a thief, A-
3

3
fraid to be caught steal-in' the land On a
night like this I start to won - der What life is all
ten.
ten.
mp
a - - bout. And I al- ways say two
Julie:
heads are bet - ter than one, to fig - ger it out.
sf

Meno mosso
Billy: (speaks) I don't need you or anyone to help me. I got it figgered out for myself. We ain't important. What
mf
are we? A couple of specks of nothin'. Look up there.
Billy: (sings)
f
There's a
a tempo
f
hell - uv- a lot o' stars in the sky And the
sky's so big the sea looks small. And
dim
p

two lit-tle peo- - ple, you and I,
rall.

We don't count at all.
a tempo
pp

Billy: You're a funny kid. Don't ever remember meetin' a girl like you.

Billy: You! Are you trying to get me to marry you? Julie: No! Billy: Then what's puttin' it into my head?

You're different all right. Don't know what it is. You look up at me with that little kid-face like — like you

trusted me. — I wonder what it'd be like. Julie: What? Billy: Nothin'! I know what it'd be like.

Allegretto moderato
Billy (speaks ad lib.) It'd be awful. I can just see myself.
Billy (sings)
Kind-a scraw - ny and
mp
sempre legato

pale, pick- in' at my food And love - sick like an - y oth - er

guy
I'd throw a-way my sweat-er And dress up like a
dude In a dick-ey and a col-lar and a tie.
If I
loved you!
Julie: (speaks)
But you don't!
Billy: (speaks)
No! I don't!
Billy: (sings)
But
Broadly
some-how I can see Just ex - act - ly how I'd be.
rall.
mf
rall.

Moderato espressivo
p a tempo
If I loved you, Time and a-gain I would try to say
p
a tempo
All I'd want you to know.
If I
loved you, Words wouldn't come in an eas-y way 'Round in
cir-cles I'd go!
Long - in' to tell you, but a-
cresc.
mf

fraid and shy. I'd let my gold-en chan-ces pass me
by. Soon you'd leave me, Off you would go in the
mist of day. Nev - er, nev - er to know
How I loved you, If I loved you!
mf molto espr.
f
mp
mf
Ped.

Billy: *(speaks)*

I'm not a feller to marry anybody — even if a girl was foolish enough to want me to, I wouldn't.

mf espr.

Julie: Don't worry about it, Billy.

Billy: Who's worried?

Julie:

You're right about there bein' no wind. The blossoms are jest comin' down by themselves.

3
3

Jest their time to, I reckon.
(The music rises ecstat-
cresc. poco a poco

ically.
Billy leans down and kisses her gently)
Curtain
ff
fff a tempo

End of Scene

Opening Act I Scene III

No. 6

June is bustin' out all over

No. 7

Cue: Carrie: .... and a nuisanse with yer yellin', and screamin' and carryin' on.

Brightly
Girls: (speak)
Voice
Piano
Give it to 'em good, Car - rie, give it to 'em good!
Carrie: (sings)
Get a-way you no ac-count noth - in's With yer sil - ly jokes and
prat - tle! If y' packed all yer brains in a but-ter-fly's head They'd
still hev room to rat - tle.
Girls: (speak)
Give it to 'em good, Car - rie,

give it to 'em Good! Tell 'em some-thin' that-'ll l'arn 'em!
Carrie: (sings)
Get a-way you roust-a-bout riff-raff; With yer bel-lies full of
mp
grog. If y' packed all yer brains in a pol-ly-wog's head He'd
nev-er ev-en grow to be a frog! The pol-ly-wog 'd nev-er be a
Girls: (sing)
f

Girls: (speak)
1st man: (sings)
frog! That-'ll l'arn 'em, darn 'em! Now jest a min - ute,
la - dies, You got no call to fret. We on - ly asked per -
2nd man:
lite - ly If you was read - y yet. We'd kind - a like this
clam-bake To git an ear - ly start, And want - ed fer to

mf
tell you We went and done our part!
Basses: Look at them clams!
2nd Tenors: All
Baritones: Been dig-gin' em since sun-up!
Basses: Look at them clams!
read-y for the boats!
1st Tenors: We're all wore out and
Basses: Look at them clams
done up!
Meno mosso
All men:
And what's more we're hun-gry as goats!
All girls:
You'll

Brightly
get no drinks er vit - tles 'till we get a - cross the bay, So
p
pull in yer belts and load them boats And let's get un - der way. The
soon - er we sail, The soon - er we start The clam - bake 'cross the
bay!
f

Meno mosso

Dialogue: **Nettie**: Here, boys! Here's some doughnuts and coffee. Fall to!

mf

(Overlapping speeches)
Doughnuts, hooray!
That's our Nettie!
Yer heart's in the right place Nettie.
Lemme in there!
Quit yer shovin'!
Nettie:
Here now, don't jump at it like you was a lotta animals in a menag'ry!

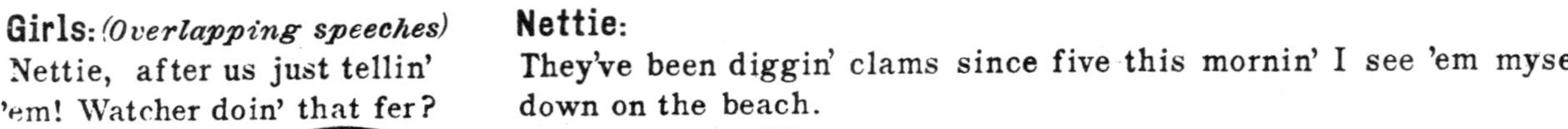
Girls: *(Overlapping speeches)*
Nettie, after us just tellin' 'em! Watcher doin' that fer?
Nettie:
They've been diggin' clams since five this mornin' I see 'em myself down on the beach.

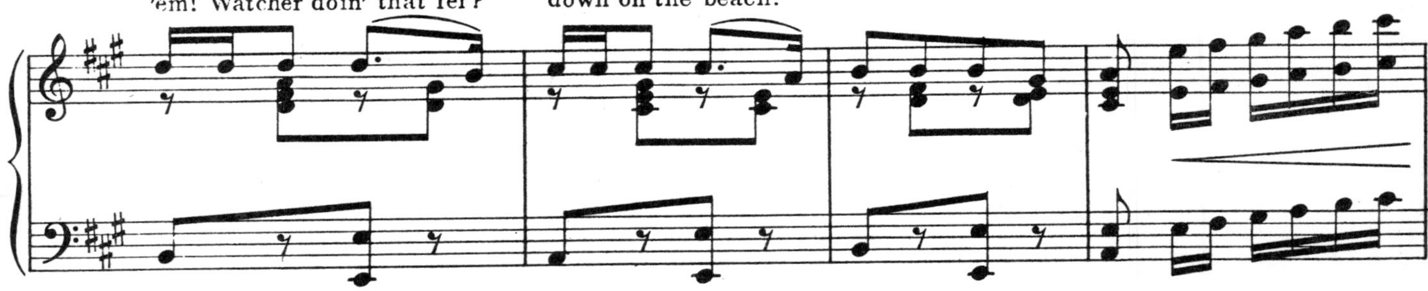

Girls:
After the way they been pesterin' and annoyin' you!
f

June is bustin' out all over

(Wait for end of dialogue) This year's jest like ev'ry other
Moderato
Nettie: (sternly)
March went out like a - li - on, A -
mf
whip-pin' up the wa-ter in the bay. Then Ap - ril cried And
stepped a - side And a - long come pret - ty lit - tle May!
May was full of prom- is - es But she did-n't keep 'em quick e-nough fer

some, And a crowd of Doubt-in' Thom-as-es Was pre-
dict-in' that the sum-mer'd nev-er come!
Men:
But it's com-in', by gum! Y' ken
mp
feel it come! Y' ken feel it in yer heart, Y' ken see it in the ground.
Girls:
Y' ken
hear it in the trees, Y' ken smell it in the breeze,
All:
Look a-round, look a-round, look a-round!
f
8
sf

Refrain (brightly)
Nettie: June is bust-in' out all o - ver, All o - ver the
Chorus: June is bust-in' out all o - ver, Solo man: The sap - lin's are
Carrie: June is bust-in' out all o - ver, The o - cean is
mp
mead-ow and the hill! Buds 're bust-in' out-a bush-es And the
bust-in' out with sap! Girl: Love has found my broth-er Jun-ior Man: And my
full of Jacks and Jills! With her lit-tle tail a-swish-in' Ev-'ry
romp-in' riv-er push-es Ev-'ry lit-tle wheel that wheels be-side a
sis-ter's ev-en lu-nier! Girl: And my Ma is get-tin' kit-ten-ish with
la-dy fish is wish-in' That a male would come and grab her by the
mill. All: June is bust-in' out all o - ver!
Pap. All: June is bust-in' out all o - ver!
gills. All: June is bust-in' out all o - ver!
f
mp

Nettie: The feel - in' is git - tin' so in - tense, That the
Nettie: To la - dies the men are pay - in' court, Lots - a
Nettie: The sheep are - n't sleep - in' an - y more, All the
young Vir - gin - ia Creep - ers Hev been hug - gin' the be - jeep - ers Out - a
ships are kept at an - chor Jest be - cause the Cap - tains hank - er Fer a
rams that chase the ewe sheep Are de - ter - mined there'll be new sheep And the
all the morn - in' glor - ies on the fence! Be - cause it's June!
com - fort they ken on - ly get in port! 2. Chorus: Be - cause it's June!
ewe - sheep are - n't ev - en keep - in' score! 3. Chorus: On a - count - a it's June!
June, June, June! Jest be - cause it's June, June,
June, June, June! Jest be - cause it's June, June,
June, June, June! Jest be - cause it's June, June,
sf
f

1.-2.
June!
June!
June!
rit.
Slowly
Nettie: Fresh and a - live and gay and young, June is a love - song
June makes the bay look bright and new, Sails gleam - in' white on
p più rit.
sweet - ly sung.
sun - lit blue.
3.
June!
sf

Encore
(June is bustin' out all over)

No. 8

Chorus:
— Be-cause it's June
June, June,
June, Jest be - cause it's June
June, June
diminuendo
diminuendo
p

Girls' Dance
(June is bustin' out all over)

No. 9

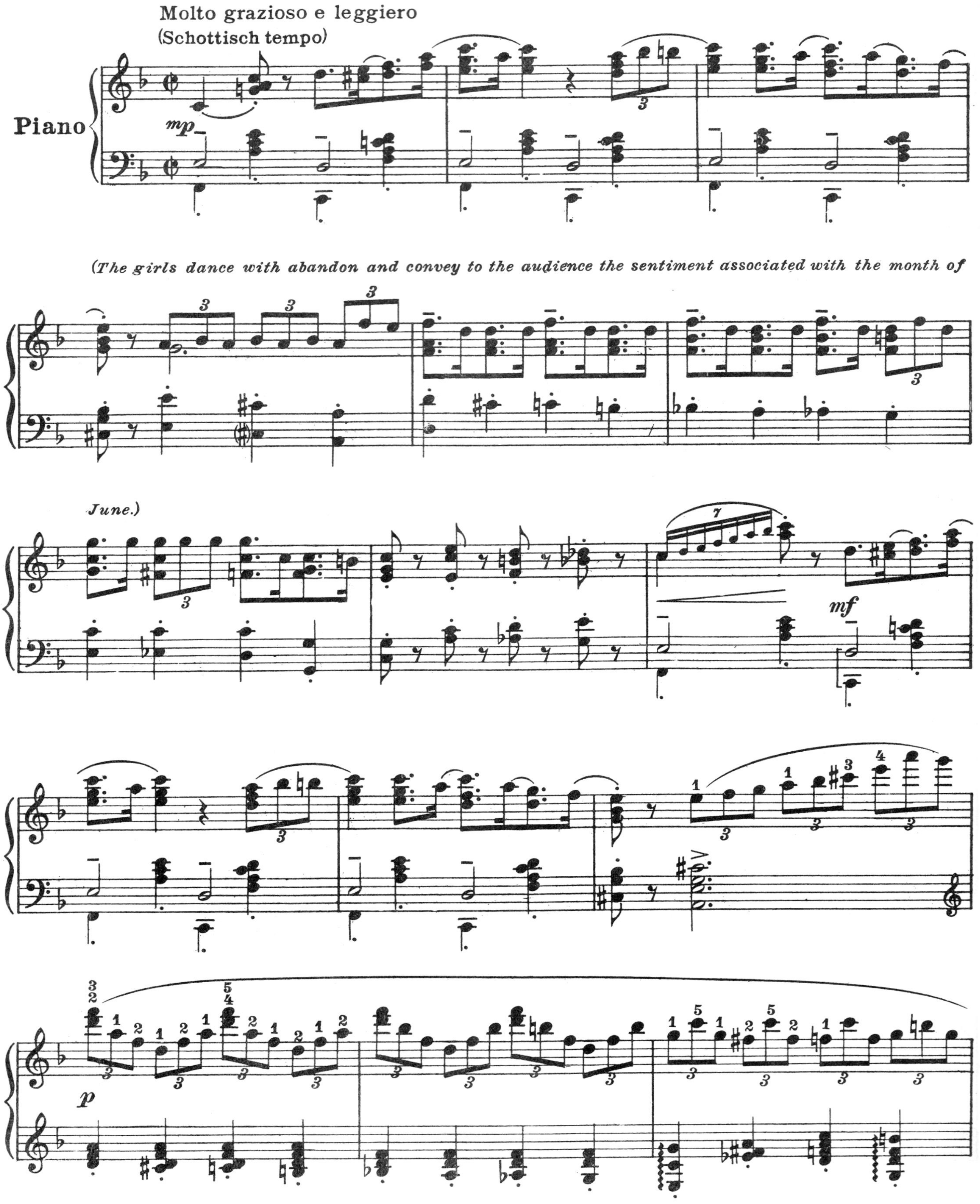

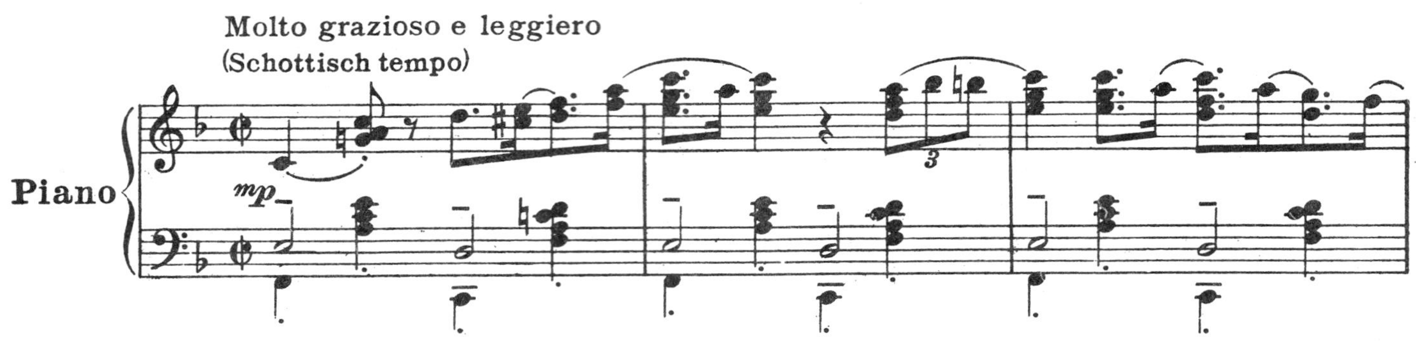

Molto grazioso e leggiero
(Schottisch tempo)
Piano
mp
(The girls dance with abandon and convey to the audience the sentiment associated with the month of
June.)
mf
p

cresc.
f
p
mf
sost.
dolce
p

p
cresc. poco a poco
f
dim. poco rit.
mf

Coda
p sub.
sf

Julie's Entrance

No. 10

Cue: After "June dance" Julie ente..

"Mr. Snow" Reprise

(Carrie, Girls, Mr. Snow)

No. 11

Cue: Girl: "I can hardly wait for the wedding"
Carrie: "Me neither"
Julie: What a day that'll be for you!

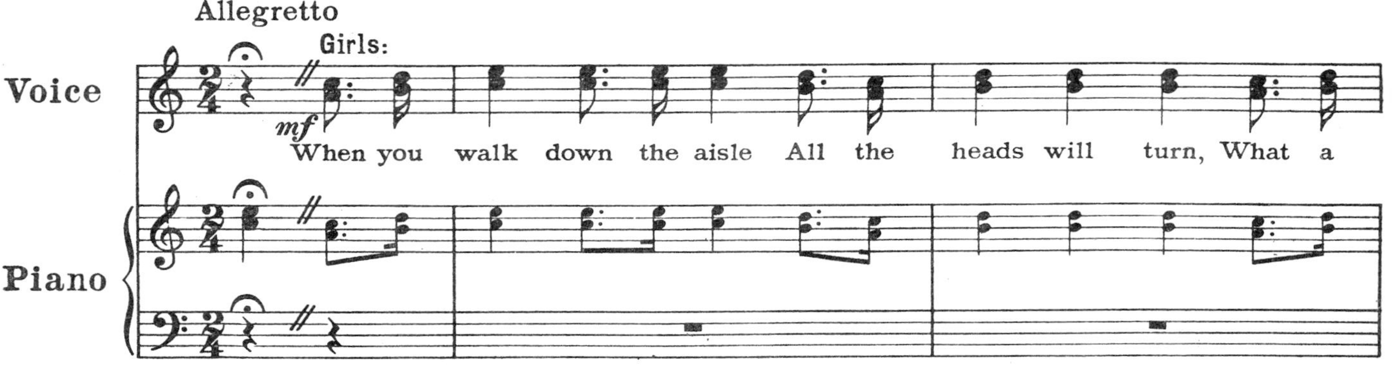

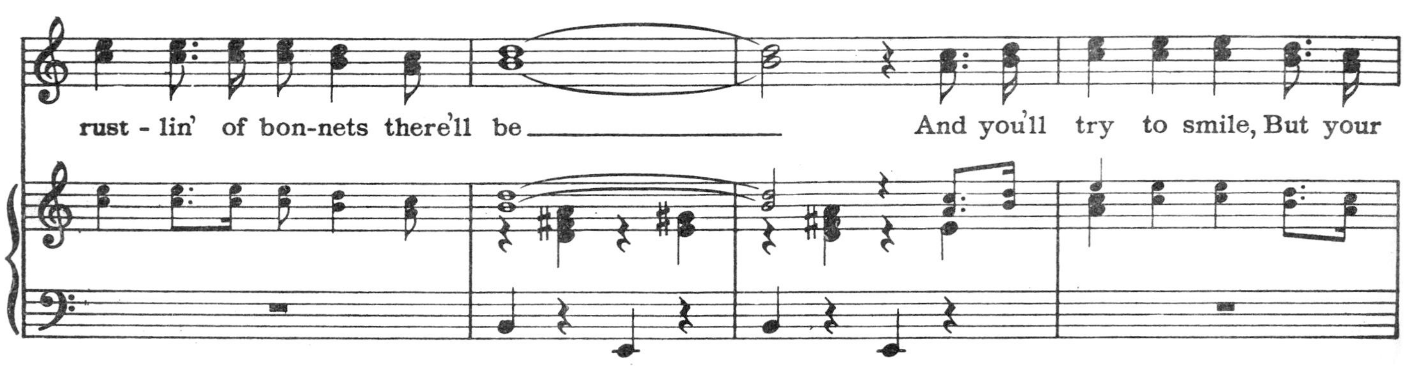

cheeks will burn And your eyes-'ll get so dim, You ken hard - ly
see!
With your or-ange blossoms quiverin' in your hand, You will
stum-ble to the spot Where the par - son is, Then your fin - ger will be ringed with a
rall.
gold - en band, And you'll know the fel-ler's yours, And you are his.
rall.

Moderato
Carrie:
When I mar - ry Mis - ter Snow
Girls: What a day, what a day!
Carrie:
The flow-ers 'll be buz-zin' with the hum of bees,
Girls:
The birds 'll make a rack-et in the church yard trees.
Carrie:
When I mar- ry Mis-ter Snow,
Girls: High - ho!
mp
Carrie:
Then it's off to home we'll go
Girls: Spil - lin' rice on the way
Carrie:
And
p

both of us will look a lit-tle dream-y-eyed A-driv-in' to a cottage by the o-cean-side,
Girls: You and Mis-ter Snow
(Snow enters)
Carrie:
Where the salt-y breez-es blow.
He'll
car-ry me 'cross the thres-hold, And I'll be as meek as a lamb, Then he'll
(Spoken)
set me on my feet And I'll say, kind-a sweet "Well Mis-ter Snow here I am!"

Mr. Snow:
Carrie: (spoken) Mister Snow!
Girls: (spoken) Mister Snow!
Snow: (sings)
Then I'll kiss her so she'll know ___ That ev'-ry thing 'll be as right as right ken be, A - liv - in' in a cot-tage by the sea with me, Where the salt-y breezes blow. ___ I love Miss Pipp'-ridge and I aim to make Miss Pipp'-ridge
rall.
Change her name to Miss - us E - noch Snow! ___
mf
mp
f
Ped.

Carrie and Mr. Snow Sequence
(When the children are asleep)

No. 12

Cue:
Mr. Snow: A man's got to make plans for his life and then he's got to stick to 'em.
Carrie: Your plans are turnin' out fine, ain't they, Enoch?

love a lit - tle girl and she's in love with me. And soon she'll be my
bride And in a man-ner of speakin' I should be sat-is -
rall.
Carrie: (Speaks)
Mr. Snow: (Sings)
fied! Well, ain't you? If I told you my plans, and the things I in - tend It 'd
p accel.
make ev - 'ry curl on yer head stand on end! When I
sf
mf

Allegretto
make e - nough mon - ey out - a one lit - tle boat, I'll put
mp leggiero
all my mon - ey in an - oth - er lit - tle boat, I'll make
twic't as much out - a two lit - tle boats and the
fust thing you know I'll hev four lit - tle boats! Then eight lit - tle boats, then a
poco a poco cresc.

fleet of lit - tle boats! Then a great, big fleet of great, big
f
boats,
accel.
All ket-chin' her-ring, bring-in' it to shore.
mf a tempo poco a poco
(with emphasis)
Sail-in' out a-gain and bring-in' in more, and more and more And
cresc.
f
ff
More!
ff accel.
sff

Dialogue

Carrie: Who's goin' t'eat all that herring?

Mr. Snow: They ain't goin' to be herring! Goin' to put them in cans and call 'em sardines. Goin'

Slowly and softly
pp

to build a little sardine cannery— then a big one— then the biggest one in the country. Carrie, I'm goin' t' get rich on sardines. I mean we're goin' t'get rich—you and me, and all of us.

rit.

Allegretto
Mr. Snow: (singing)
The fust year we're mar-ried we'll hev one lit - tle kid, The
mf
leggiero

sec - ond year we'll go and hev an - oth - er lit - tle kid, You'll

Carrie:
soon be darn-in' socks fer eight lit-tle feet. Are you build-in' up to an-
cresc.
f
oth - er fleet?
accel.
accel.
Mr. Snow:
We'll build a lot more
p a tempo
rooms, Our dear lit - tle house 'll get big - ger, our
dear lit - tle house 'll get big - ger! And so will my fig - ger.
Carrie:

Dialogue.

Mr. Snow: Carrie, ken y'imagine how it'll be when all thé kids are upstairs in bed, and you and me sit alone in the firelight?

Moderato (slowly)
Me in my armchair— you on my knee— mebbe?
Carrie: Mebbe.
Moderato con moto
When the chil-dren are a - sleep, we'll sit and dream
The things that ev - 'ry oth - er dad and moth-er dream.
When the chil-dren are a - sleep and lights are low.
If I still

love you The way I love you to - day, You'll
par - don my say - ing: "I told you so!"
When the chil-dren are a - sleep I'll dream with you. We'll think, what
fun we hev had and be glad that it all came true!
mf
rall.
f

Moderato
Carrie:
mf
p
When chil-dren are a-wake, A-romp-in thru the rooms and
run-nin' on the stairs
Then in a man-ner of speak-in' A
house is real-ly theirs
But once they close their eyes, And
we are left a.-lone And free from all their fuss,

Then in a man-ner of speak-in' We can be real-ly us.
Carrie:
When the chil-dren are a - sleep, We'll sit and dream, The things that
Mr. Snow:
Dream all a - lone.
mp
ev - 'ry oth - er Dad and Mother dream.
Dreams that won't be in - ter-rupt-ed

Carrie:
Lo! And be - hold. If I still
When the chil-dren are a - sleep And lights are low
love you the way I love you to - day You'll par-don my say - ing:
"I told you so!" When the children are a - sleep I'll dream with you,
Mr. Snow:
You'll dream with
mf

We'll think what fun we hev had And be glad that it all came true.
me.
When to-day is a long time a-go. You'll still hear me say that the
You'll still hear me say that the
mp
poco espress.
poco rit.
a tempo
best dream I know is: When the children are a-sleep I'll dream with you!
best dream I know is you!
l.h.
mf

Blow High, Blow Low

No. 13

Jigger: Hey, Billy! Where you goin'? Stick with me. After we get rid of my shipmates I wanta talk
ppp (very softly under dialogue)
— Blow high, blow low! — A-whal-in' we go! We'll go a-
ppp
to you. Got an idea for you and me to make money. Billy: How much? Jigger: More'n you ever saw in yer
whal-in' a-sail-in' a-way. A-way we'll go, (Blow me high and
life. Man: Hey Jigger, come back here! Jigger: Come on Billy.
low!) For man-y and man-y a long, long day, — For man y— and
man-y— a long, long day! —

Jigger:
The peo-ple who live on land Are hard to un-der-stand, When you're look-in' for fun They clap you in-to jail, So I'm ship-pin' off to sea, Where life is gay and free, And a fel-ler can flip A hook in the hip of a whale.
All men:
Blow high, Blow low! A-

whal - in' we will go, We'll go a - whal - in' a - sail - in' a -
way. A - way we'll go, (Blow me high and low!) For
man - y and man - y a long, long day, For man - y and
man - y a long, long day!
f
f
8

Billy:
It's won-der-ful just to feel Your hands up-on a wheel, And to
p
lis-ten to wind a-whist-lin' in a sail! Or to climb a-loft and
mf
p
be The ver-y first to see A chrys-anthemum sprout come out of the snout of a
All men:
f
whale! Blow high, Blow low, A-whal-in' we will
f
ff

go! We'll go a - whal - in' a - sail - in' a - way. A -
way we'll go, (Blow me high and low!) For man-y and man-y a
As the singing proceeds, some of the girls and
men drift in, more sailors enter.
long, long day, For man - y and man - y a long,
long day!
Jigger:
pp
A -

rock-in' up-on the sea, Your boat will seem to be Like a
p
dear lit-tle ba-by in her bass-in-et, For she has-n't learned to
mf
p
walk And she has-n't learned to talk, And her lit-tle be-hind Is
3
3
All men:
f
kind-a in-clined to be wet! Blow high, Blow low! A-
f
ff

whal - in' we will go! We'll go a - whal - in' a - sail - in' a -
way. A - way we'll go Blow me high and low, For
man - y and man - y a long, long day,
For man - y and man - y a
(finish with big vocal climax)
long, long day!
ten.
ten.
gliss
sff
ff

Hornpipe

No. 14

Allegro
Piano
f
Sailors and fishermen start to dance a Hornpipe. The women try to attract their attention and join the
dance, but are ignored and snubbed by the men.
mf

f
p
cresc. poco a poco
f
8
8
ff

The women wave their handkerchiefs and coquette with the men, but withdraw timidly. Both groups stand watching one another at opposite sides of the stage.

1st fisherman:
"Thar she blows!"
2nd fisherman:
"H'ist yer mud 'ook!"
3rd fisherman:
Spread your sails and get under weigh!"
4th fisherman:
"Looks like a rowboat ridin' up to a lighthouse!"
Several men:
"Kedge! Luff! Scud!"
A girl:
"Go it Hannah!"
5th fisherman:
"Release your davits and jump!"
A girl:
"Keep afloat!"
Optional repeat until cue
The tallest sailor steps out of the group to dance with Hannah.
Wood block

Dance danced between Hannah and sailor.
p leggiero
ff
8
p
2
ff
mf
8
sempre stacc.
1

f
1
p
4
ff
8
mf
Group joins in.
cresc. poco a poco
8
8
8
ff

ff
f
ff
marc.
ff

8
8
19 bars rest, strictly in time
(dance continues in silence)
f
ff

Men leave. They run back to the sea.
The women left deserted wave forlornly.
dim.
molto
mf
Hannah continues dancing
in the hope her man will return.
accel.
dim.
poco
a
poco
Her sailor returns and carries her off.
r.h.
pp
f
r.h.
l.h.
8
ff
For Exit
repeat first 12 bars from
page 101 until dialogue
gliss
sff

Cue: Billy: *(Kicks Mrs. Mullin)* Get the hell out of here! *(Turns to cottage and comes down stage.)*

Soliloquy

No. 15

more com-mon sence Than his pud-din' head-ed fa-ther ev-er had.
I'll
f
accel.
Più mosso
teach him to wras-sle, And dive through a wave, When we go in the morn-in's for our
mf
swim. His moth-er can teach him The way to be-have, But she
won't make a sis-sy out o' him. Not him! Not my boy! Not
rit.
rit.

a tempo
(Speaks)
Bill! ___
Bill!
Allegro
My boy, Bill! (I will see that he's named af - ter me, ___
___ I will!)
My boy, Bill! He'll be
tall And as tough as a tree, ___
Will Bill! ___

— Like a tree he'll grow, With his head held high And his
feet plant-ed firm on the ground, And you won't see
no - bod - y dare to try To boss him or toss him a -
round! No pot - bel - lied, bag - gy eyed bul - ly 'll boss him a -
poco allarg.
sf
f marcato e poco allarg.

Con moto
round.
I don't give a damn what he
f a tempo
mf
does,
As long as he does what he
likes!
He can sit on his tail, Or
work on a rail With a hammer, a-hammer-in' spikes.
He can
fer-ry a boat on a river, Or ped-dle a pack on his

back. Or work up and down The streets of a town With a
whip and a horse and a hack. He can haul a scow a-
long a canal, Run a cow a-round a cor-ral, Or may-be bark for a
car-rou-sel Of course it takes tal-ent to do that well. He
f
rit.
colla voce
mf

a tempo
might be a champ of the heav - y-weights, Or a fel - ler that sells you
a tempo
glue, ___ Or Pres-i-dent of the U - nit - ed States That-'d be al - right,
(Speaks ad lib.)
too.___
His mother would like that_But he wouldn't be
mp
(Sings)
President unless he wanted to be. Not Bill!
marcato
f

My boy, Bill! He'll be tall And as tough As a tree,
Will Bill!
Like a tree he'll grow, With his
head held high, And his feet plant-ed firm on the ground,
And you won't see no-bod-y dare to try To
mf

boss him or toss him a - round! No fat bot - tomed,
sf
f marcato e poco allarg.
8
flab - by - faced, pot - bel - lied, bag - gy - eyed bas - tard 'll boss him a -
Poco più mosso
round.
And I'm damned if he'll mar-ry his
f
mf
boss - 's daugh-ter, A skin-ny lipped vir-gin with blood like wa-ter. Who'll

rall.
(Speaks)
give him a peck And call it a kiss, And look in his eyes through a lorg-net Say,
rall.
sf
(Sings)
(laugh)
Why am I tak - in' on like this? My kid aint ev - en been born yet!
mf ad lib.
a tempo
Moderato (slower)
I can see him when he's sev - en - teen or so And start-in' in to
mf
go with a girl! I can give him Lots of point-ers,

ve - ry sound, On the way to get 'round an - y girl.
a tempo
(Speaks)
I can tell him— Wait a min - ute!— Could it be? What the
rit.
Hell! What if he is a girl?
Original tempo
(Speaks utterly heart-broken by the thought)
Bill - - Oh, Bill!
What would I do with her? What could I do for her? A bum with no money!
(Sings)
You can have
mp

fun with a son, But you got to be a fa-ther To a girl!
She might-n't be so bad at that, A kid with
rib-bons In her hair! A kind o' neat and pe-tite Lit-tle
tin-type of her moth-er! What a pair!
(Spoken) I can just hear myself bragging about her!
mp
f

Broader (with warmth)
My lit-tle girl, Pink and white As peach-es and cream is she.
mf
My lit-tle girl Is half a-gain as bright As girls are meant to be!
Doz-ens of boys pur - sue her, Man-y a like - ly lad
Does what he can to woo her From her faith - ful dad.

She has a few Pink and white young fel-lers of two and three But
my lit-tle girl Gets hun-gry ev-'ry night and she comes home to
Poco più mosso
(Spoken) My little girl, my little girl!
me! I got to get read-y be-
fore she comes! I got to make cer-tain that she Won't be dragged up in slums With a
mf
poco a
poco cresc.

Attacca Finale

Finale Act I

No. 16

Cue: Nettie enters

Nettie: Hey, you roustabouts! Time to get goin'! Come and help us carry everythin' on the boats. **1st Man:** All right, Nettie, we're comin'!

2nd Man: Don't need to hev a fit about it. **Nettie:** Hey, Billy! What's this Julie says about you not goin' to the clambake? **Billy:** Clambake? Mebbe I will go—after all! There's Jigger! I got to talk to him! Hey Jigger!

Come here—quick! **Nettie:** I'll tell Julie you're comin'. She'll be tickled pink. *(She exits.)* *Jigger (comes on)* **Billy:** Jigger! I changed my mind! You know—about goin' to the clambake and—

I'll do everythin' like you said. Gotta get money on account of the baby—see?

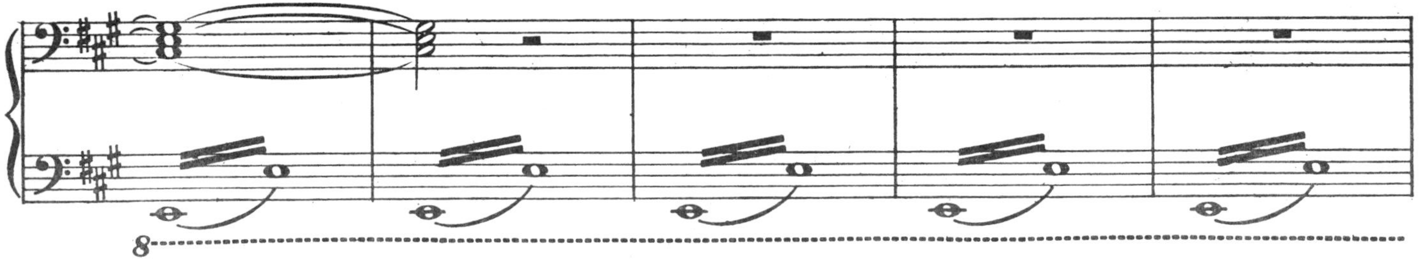

Jigger: Sure the baby! Did you get a knife? **Billy:** Knife? **Jigger:** I only got a pocket knife. If he shows fight we'll need a real one.

Billy: But I ain't got— **Jigger:** Go inside and take the kitchen knife. **Billy:** Somebody might see me— **Jigger:** Take it so they don't see you! **Julie:** *(entering)* Billy is it true?

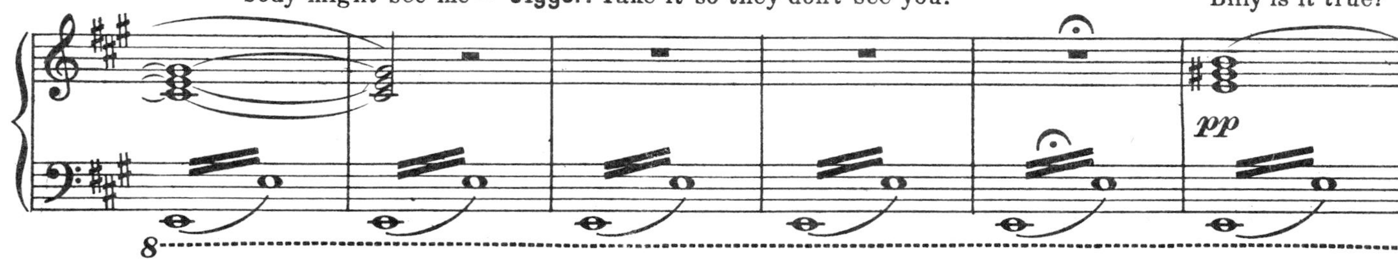

Are you comin' to the clambake? **Billy:** I think so. Yes— **Julie:** We'll have a barrel of fun. I'll show you all over the island. Know every inch of it. Been goin' to picnics there

since I been a little girl. **Jigger:** Billy! Billy! Y' better go and get that— **Julie:** Get what, Billy? **Billy:** Why— *(Chorus enters)* **Jigger:** The shawl. Billy said you oughter have a shawl. Gets

cold at nights. Fog comes up— ain't that what you said? **Billy:** Y-yes. I better go and get it—the shawl. **Julie:** Now that was real thoughtful, Billy! **Billy:** I'll go and get it! **Nettie:** C'mon all!

Brightly
Chorus:
June is bust - in' out all o - ver The
flow - ers are bust - in' from their seed.
Nettie:
And the
pleas - ant life of Ri - ley, That is spok - en of so
high - ly, Is the life that ev - 'ry - bod - y wants to
mf

Chorus:(all)
lead! Be-cause it's June!
June, June, June! Jest be - cause it's
(They start to exit)
June, June, June! Be-cause it's June,
Be-cause it's June, Be-cause it's June,

Be-cause it's June!
dim.
mf
dim. sempre
sff

Entr'act

No 17

f
ff
molto rit.
r.h.
l.h.
pp

Andante con moto
cantabile
p
sopra
mf
dolce
poco accel.

rall.
f a tempo
poco accel. e cresc.
f rit.
Broadly
f
accel. poco a poco
ff
poco rit.

Allegro
f

dim.
Moderato
mf
f
p

f
dim.
Meno mosso
mf
f
Allargando
f
accel.
8
ff

Opening Act II

No. 18

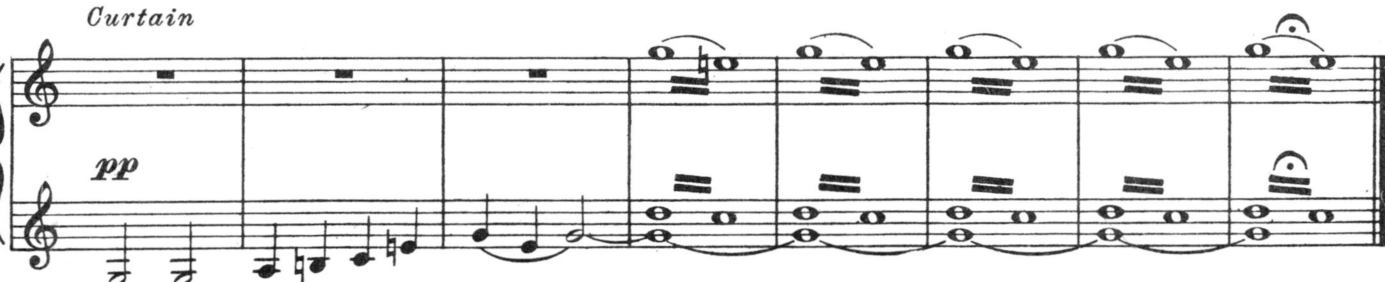

A real nice clambake

No. 19

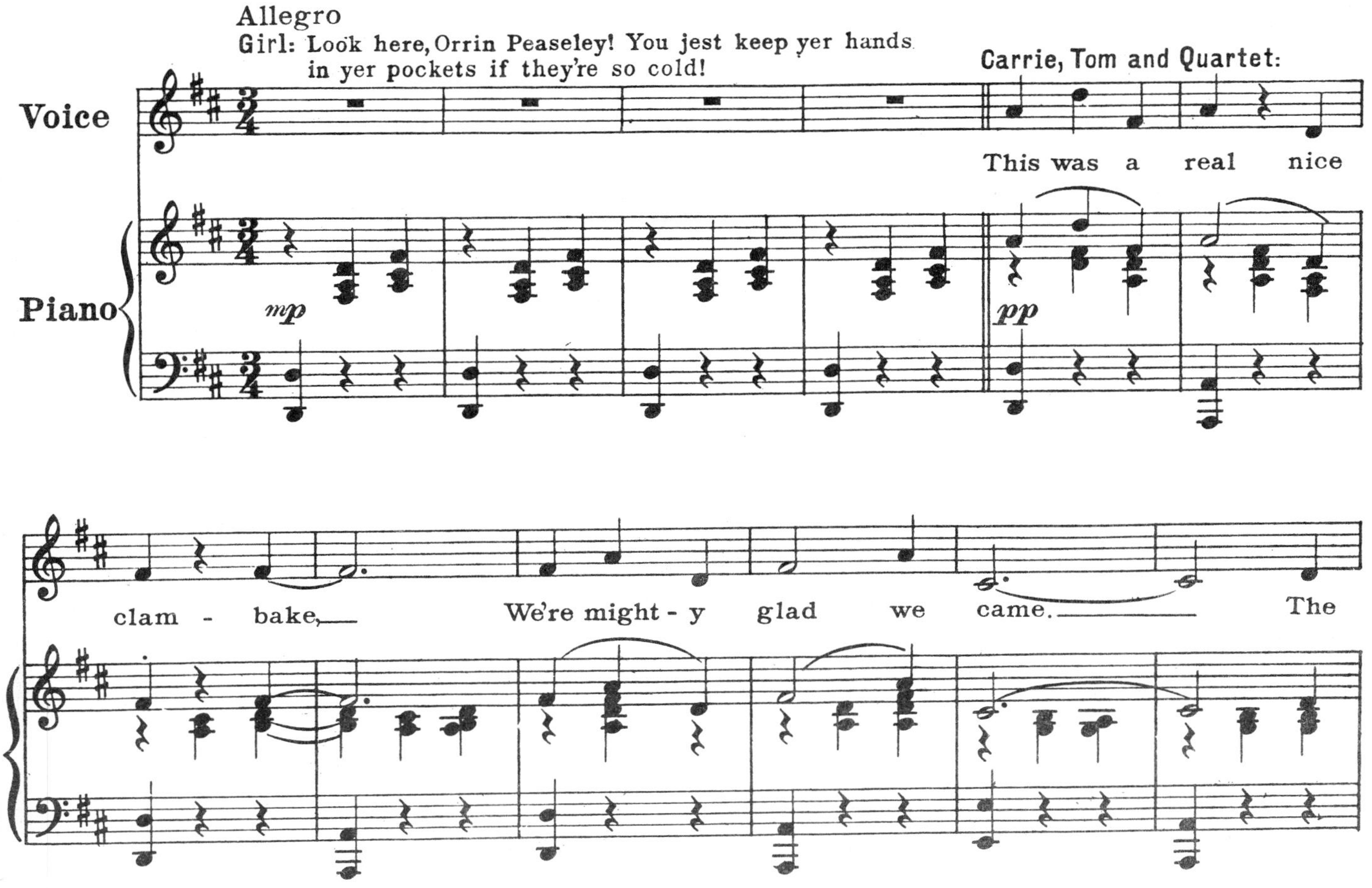

Allegro

Girl: Look here, Orrin Peaseley! You jest keep yer hands in yer pockets if they're so cold!

Carrie, Tom and Quartet:

Voice

Piano

mp

pp

This was a real nice clam - bake,___ We're might - y glad we came.___ The

vit- tles we et Were good, you bet! The com-pan- y was the
same. Our hearts are warm, our bel- lies are full And
we are feel - in' prime. This was a real nice
clam - bake And we all hed a real good time!

Nettie:
Fust come cod-fish chow-der
Cooked in i-ron ket-tles,
On-ions float-in' on the top,
Curl-in' up in pet-als!
Julie:
Throwed in ri-bons of salt-ed pork
All men:
(An old New
mf
mp

Julie:
Eng - land trick) And lapped it all up with a clam - shell,
Tied on to a bay-ber-ry stick!
All:
Oh!
f
All:
This was a real nice clam - bake, We're might - y glad we
f
came. The vit - tles we et Were good, you bet! The

com - pan - y was the same.
Our hearts are
warm, Our bel - lies are full And we are feel - in'
prime.
This was a real nice clam - bake
And we all hed a real good time!
Mr. Snow:
Re -

mem-ber when we raked Them red hot lob-sters Out of the drift-wood fire? They
siz-zled and crackled And sput-tered a song, Fit-ten fer an an-gels' choir!
All girls:
Fit-ten fer an an-gels', Fit-ten fer an an-gels', Fit-ten fer an an-gels' choir!
Nettie:
We
slit 'em down the back And pep-pered 'em good, And doused 'em in melt-ed but-ter, Then we
Carrie:
p
f
mf poco allarg.

tore a-way the claws And cracked 'em with our teeth 'Cause we were-n't in a mood to put-ter!
All girls:
Fit-ten fer an an-gels', Fit-ten fer an an-gels', Fit-ten fer an an-gels' choir!
f a tempo
Religioso
Baritone Solo:
Then at last, come the clams
Men:
Steamed un-der rock-weed And
p
pop-pin' from their shells.
All:
Jest how man-y of 'em Gal-loped down our gul-lets

Allegro
All:
We could-n't say our - sel's! OH - - H - - H
mf
cresc.
This was a real nice clam - bake,
We're might - y glad we
f
came!
The vit - tles we et Were good, you bet! The
com-pan - y was the same.
Our hearts are warm Our

bel - lies are full And we are feel - in prime.
This was a real nice clam - bake,
Girls:
And we all hed a real good time! We
TENOR I, II
And we all hed a real good time! We
BAR., BASS
And we all hed a real good time! We

said it a - fore And we'll say it a - gen, We
said it a - fore And we'll say it a - gen, We
said it a - fore And we'll say it a - gen, We
ff
all hed a real good time!
all hed a real good time!
all hed a real good time!
ff
sff

Geraniums in the winder
(and "Stonecutters cut it on stone")

No. 20

Cue: Mr. Snow: Leave me to my shattered dreams.
They are all I have left, memories of what didn't happen.

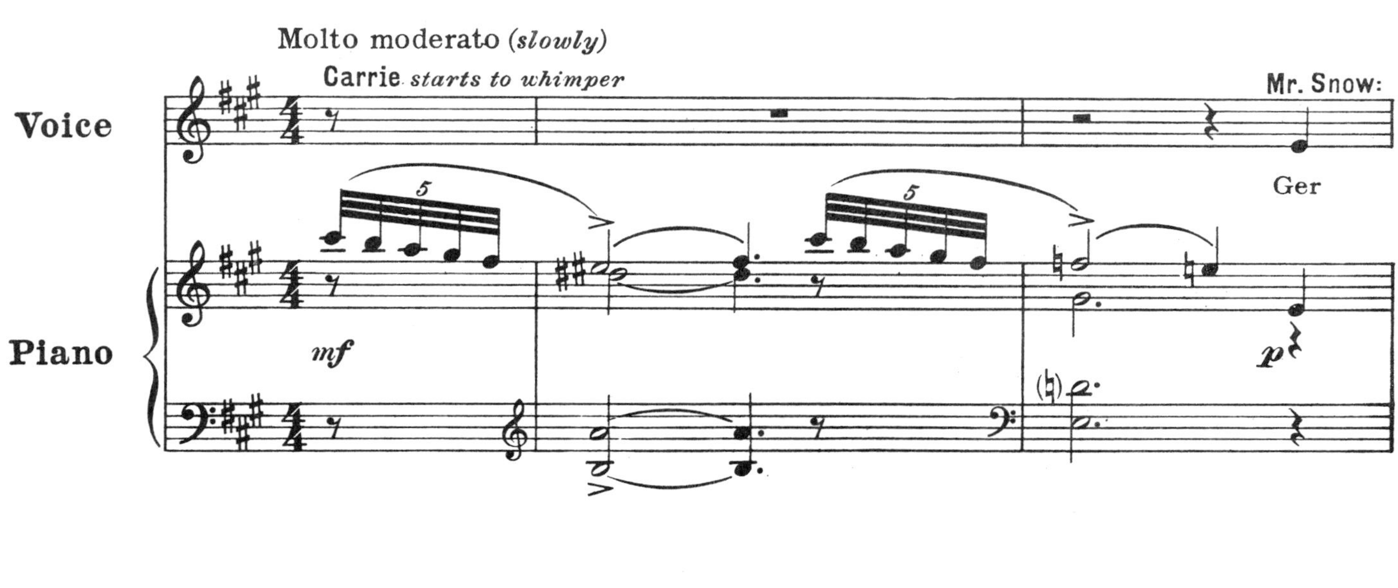

you to blow me kiss-es When I head-ed fer the sea. We
might hev been a hap-py pair of lov-ers, Might-n't hev we?
mf
5
5
mp
And com-in' home at twi-light It
might hev been so sweet To take my ketch of her-ring And

lay them at your feet! I might hev had a
Jigger: Snow:
(spoken) (sings)
ba - by, What? To dan - dle on my knee, But all these things That
rit.
might hev been, are nev - er, nev - er to be!
mf
Carrie blows and her tone-pitch when she cries is strangely similar to the one of the orchestra.
(A few people enter)
Jigger: (sings)
1. I

Allegretto
nev - er see it yet to fail, I nev - er see it
Moth - er used to say to me, "When you grow up my
mp leggiero
fail! A girl who's in love with a vir - tu - ous man, Is
son, I hope you're a bum like your fa - ther was Cause a
doomed to weep and wail!
good man ain't no fun!"
Stone cut - ters cut it on
sf
mp
Chorus:
(2nd time)
stone, Wood peck - ers pick it on wood, There's

noth - in' so bad fer a wom - an As a man who thinks he's
1.
(Carrie bawls)
Mr. Snow: (speaks) Nice talk!
good!
mf
Jigger:
2. My
2.
Mr. Snow:
good! 'Tain't
Jigger: (going lower)
Snow's chorus: (lower)
Jigger's chorus: (lower)
so! 'Tis too! 'Tain't so! 'Tis too!
Dialogue

(After dialogue)

Cue: **Carrie:** And he was a different person.

Allegretto
All girls:
God knows what-in all night! Stone cut-ters cut it on stone,
sf
mf a tempo
Wood-peck-ers peck it on wood, There's noth-in' so bad for a wom-an As a
man who's bad or good!
Dialogue:
Carrie: It makes you wonder don't it?
Girls: What do you think, Julie? You tell her Julie! She's your best girlfriend.
Allegretto
Girls: (rhythmically spoken)
Tell it to her good, Jul-ie,
mf
Tell it to her good!
f
rall.

What's the use of wond'rin'

No. 21

Assai moderato
Julie: (softly and earnestly)
Voice
Piano
What's the use of won-d'rin if he's good or if he's bad, Or
if you like the way he wears his hat?
Oh! what's the use of won-d'rin', If he's
good or if he's bad? He's your fel-ler and you love him.
That's all there is to

that.
Com-mon sense may tell you, That the
mf
p
end - in' will be sad, And now's the time to break and run a -
way. But what's the use of won-d'rin' if the end - in' will be sad? He's your
fel - ler and you love him - There's noth-in more to say.
mf

Some-thin' made him the way that he is,
Wheth-er he's false or true And some-thin' gave him the
things that are his One of those things is you. So
when he wants your kiss-es you will give them to the lad, And
mp
mf
p

an - y-where he leads you, you will walk and an - y-time he needs you, you'll go
run - nin' there like mad! You're his girl and he's your fel - ler
And all the rest is "talk!"
(Billy and Jigger enter)
Julie: (speaks)
Billy! where you goin'?
Billy:
Where we goin'?
Jigger:
We're lookin' for the treasure.
Julie: I don't want you to, Billy Let me come with you.
mp

(Julie feels knife inside Billy's vest)
Jigger: No!
Julie: Billy!
Billy: I got no time to fool with women.
Julie: Let me have that! Oh Billy please.
mp
mf
All Girls: (sings)
Com - mon sense may tell you that the end - in' will be sad, And
mf
now's the time to break and run a - way, But what's the use of won-d'rin' if the
end - in' will be sad? He's your fel - ler and you love him

Curtain
There's noth - in' more to say.
p
pp

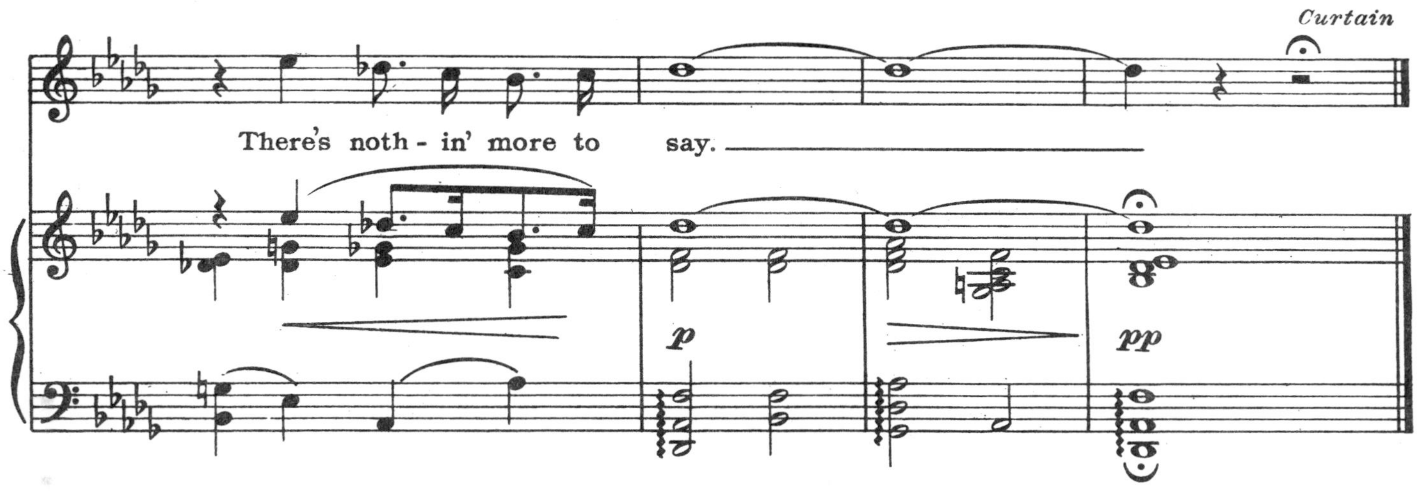

Change of Scene

(Act II. Scene 2)

No. 22

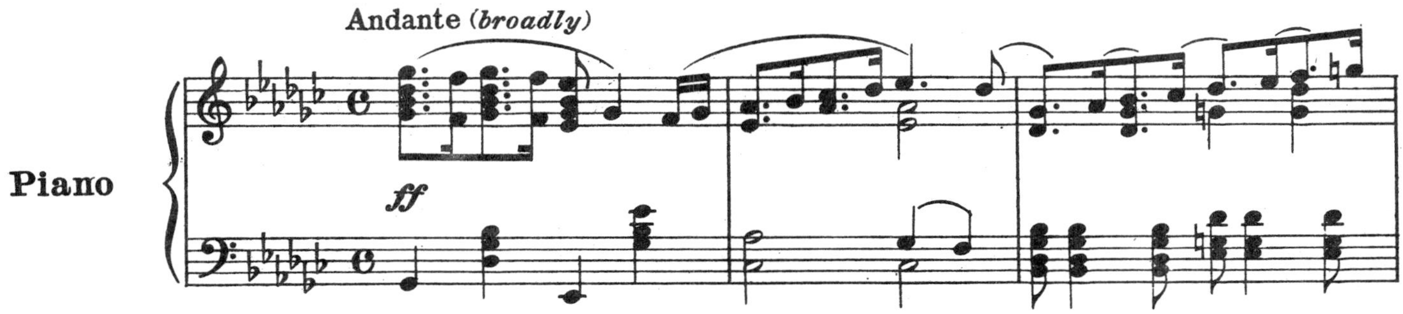

Andante (broadly)
Piano
ff

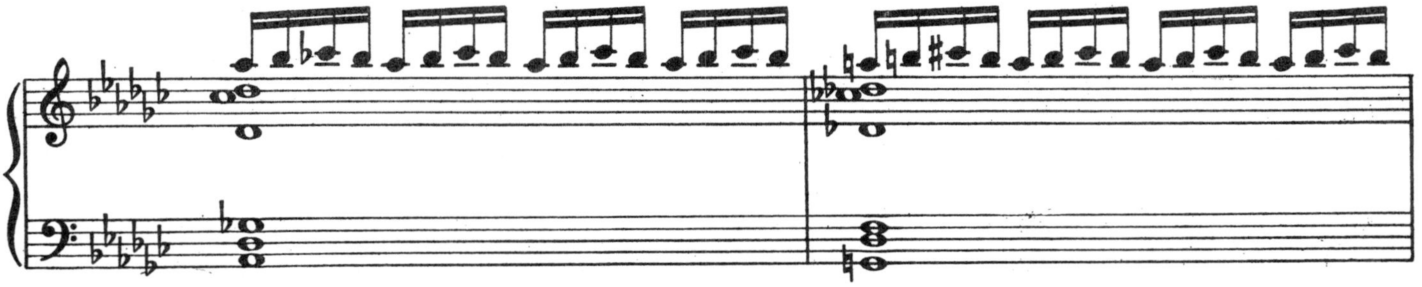

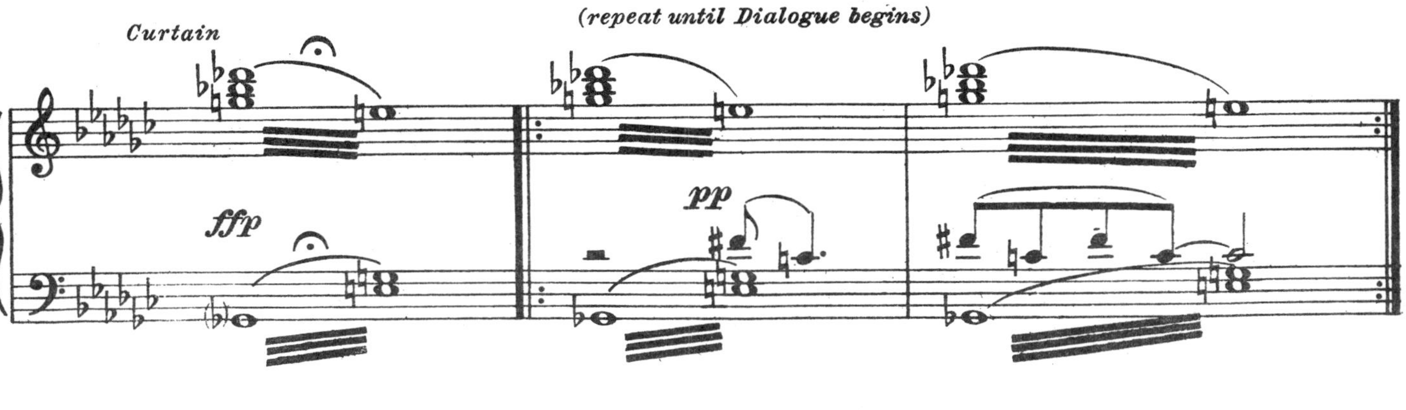

Curtain
(repeat until Dialogue begins)
ffp
pp

You'll never walk alone

No. 23

Cue: Julie: The words? I used to say 'em in school.
Nettie: Say 'em now–see if you know what they mean.

chin up high And don't be a - fraid of the
dark.
At the end of the storm is a
gold - en sky And the sweet sil - ver song of a
rall.
lark.
Walk on through the wind, Walk
mf

on through the rain, Tho' your dreams be tossed and

blown, Walk on, walk on, with

cresc. poco a poco

hope in your heart, And you'll nev - er walk a -

f sempre cresc.

lone, You'll nev - er walk a - lone!

più cresc.

ff with great expression

allarg.

Incidental

No. 24

(Entrance of Heavenly Friend)

Heavenly Friend (enters): Get up, Billy.
Billy: Huh?
Hea. Fr: Get up!
Billy: Who are you?
Hea. Fr: Shake yourself up. Got to get goin'.
Billy: Goin'? Where?
Moderato
Piano
p
Hea. Fr: Never mind where, important thing is, you can't stay there.
Billy: Julie!
Hea. Fr: She can't hear you.
Billy: Who decided that?
Hea. Fr: You did when you killed yourself. (A curtain of stars comes down)
Billy: I see! So it's over!
Hea. Fr: It isn't as simple as that. As long as there's one person on earth who remembers you, it isn't over.
Billy: What are you goin' to do to me?
Hea. Fr: We ain't goin' to do anythin', we just come down to fetch you, take you up to the judge.
Billy: Judge! I'm goin' before the Lord God himself?
Hea. Fr: What hev you ever

Billy:

done that you should come before Him? So that's it. Just like Jiggers said. No supreme court for little people— just po-

Hea. Fr: **Billy:**

lice magistrates! Who said anything about? I tell you if they kick me around up there like they did on earth, I'm goin'

to do somethin' about it! I'm dead and I got nothin' to lose and I'm goin' to stand up for my rights! I'm tellin' you I'm go-

Hea. Fr:

in' before the Lord Himself— straight to the top! Y' hear? Simmer down, Billy. Simmer down.

The Highest Judge of all

No. 25

Moderato marcato
Voice
Piano
Billy:
r.h.
ff
mf deciso
Take me be-yond the pearl-y gates, Through a beau-ti-ful mar-ble hall. Take me be-fore the high-est throne And let me be judged by the high-est Judge of all!
Let the Lord shout and yell, And his eyes flash flame, I

prom-ise not to quiv-er when he calls my name. Let him send me to hell, But be-
fore I go, I feel that I'm en-ti-tled to a hell of a show!
f
Want pink-faced angels on a pur-ple cloud,
p
Twang-in' on their harps till their fin-gers get red. Want or-gan mu-sic, let it
cresc.

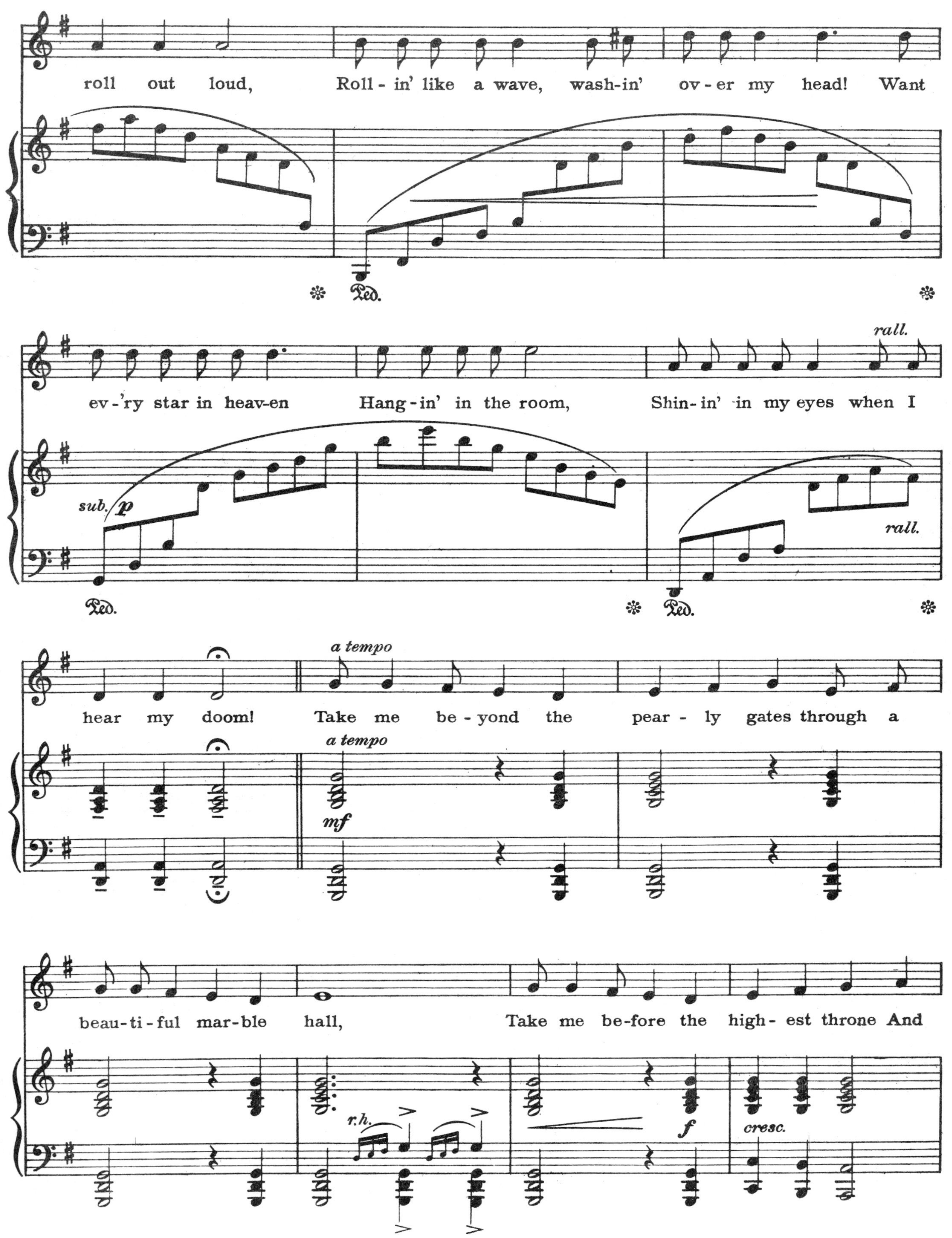
roll out loud, Roll - in' like a wave, wash-in' ov - er my head! Want
Ped.
ev - 'ry star in heav-en Hang - in' in the room, Shin - in' in my eyes when I
rall.
sub. p
rall.
Ped.
Ped.
hear my doom! Take me be - yond the pear - ly gates through a
a tempo
a tempo
mf
beau - ti - ful mar - ble hall, Take me be - fore the high - est throne And
r.h.
f
cresc.

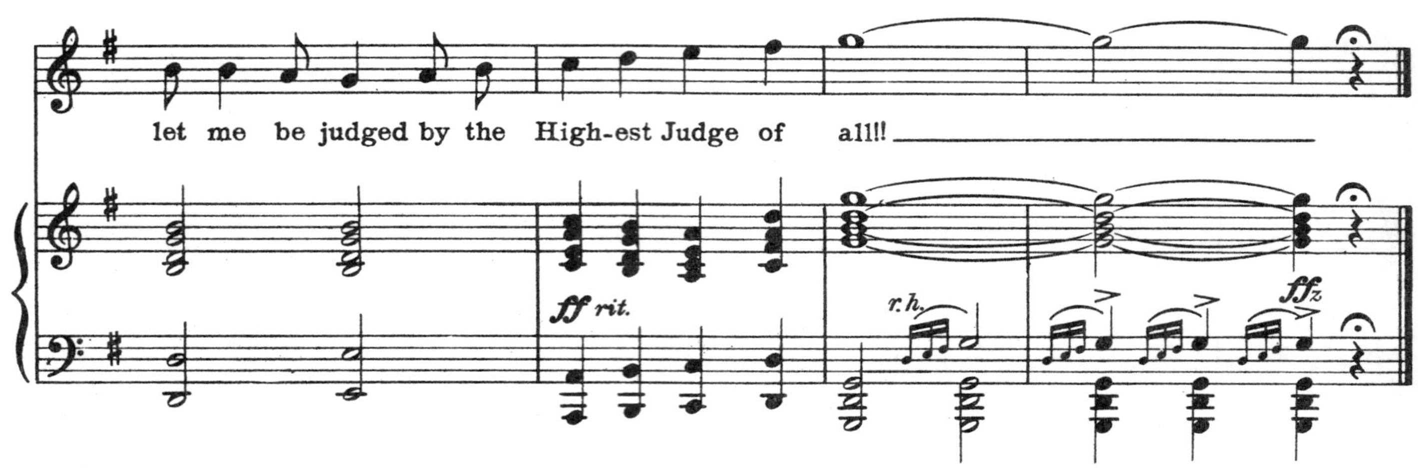
let me be judged by the High-est Judge of all!!
ff rit.
r.h.
ffz

Exit of Billy and Heavenly Friend

(Change of Scene)

No. 26

L'istesso tempo

Piano

ff

r.h.

p

pp

(Fade out)

Cue: **Billy**: Where is she? What do I have to do to see her?

Ballet

No. 27

Introduction to Ballet
Star Keeper: Jest look down and wait. The power to see her will come to you Billy: Is that her?
Lento
Piano
pp dolce
Little kid with straw colored hair? Pretty ain't she? My little girl! Blackout
8
pp

Ballet begins here:

The daughter, Louise, is discovered standing alone on the beach in full morning light. She runs and leaps and tumbles in animal joy.

Con moto

f

f sempre
8
ff

She turns a somersault and lies down on the sand to stare at the sky.
Allegro giocoso
Two ragged urchins come in leap-frogging.
mp
She joins them in their rough play.
1
Poco meno mosso
mf
f
f sempre

f sempre
Mr. Snow enters followed by six little Snows in Sunday hats in single file.
mf (gaily)
p
They stop in amazement to see the boisterous

rough-housing of Louise and her companions. Mr. Snow strongly disapproves.

Louise asks them to play with her.
mf
f
8
They snub her and leave.
8
sf
mf
8
8
f
sf
A younger Miss Snow lags behind out of curiosity. She examines Louise's poor dress and bare feet
f

with unfriendly dislike. Miss Snow is stuck up.

pp

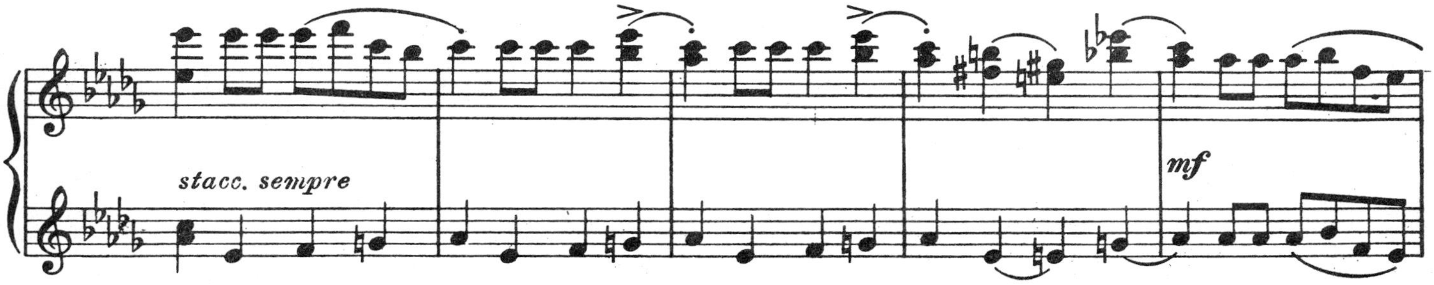

stacc. sempre

mf

cresc.

f

The children speak:

Miss Snow: My father bought me my pretty dress.

Louise: My father would have bought me a pretty dress too. He was a barker at a carousel.

Miss Snow: Your father was a thief.

Louise chases her in a rage and steals her fancy hat. The boys approve.

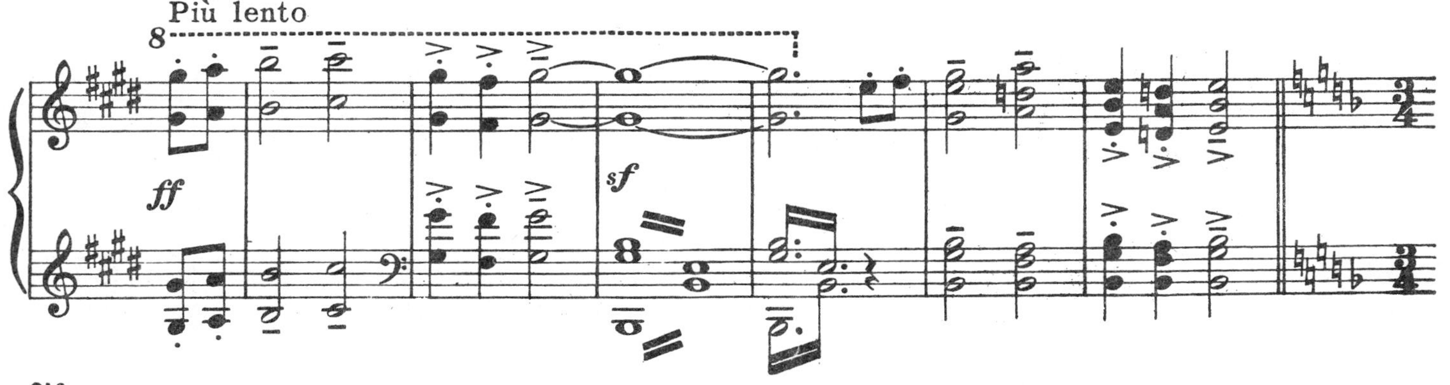

Waltz tempo
A carnival troup comes in, headed by a young man who is like what Louise believes
sf
tr
mf
Drum roll.
her father to have been. She is enchanted and excited by their costumes. She snitches the gold parasol
of the leading acrobatic lady.
ff
The carniaval people perform a brutal and frenetic
f
8
Waltz
1.
2.
8

p
cresc.
8
sf
ff
8
8
8
loco
f

The acrobat lady sees Louise holding the stolen parasol and demands it back. The young man and Louise
dim.
meet face to face. He tells her not to mind and winks at her.
The carnival people exit
f
marc.
dim.
4
mf

Louise is alone on the beach with the young man who has waited behind.

Andante, ma non troppo

espr.

mf dolce

dim.

p poco rit.

He makes love to her. In spite of herself she is drawn toward him.

Andante
f dolce

He grows frightened at her intensity. Realizing she is only a child he leaves her and goes away.

She feels humiliated

and ashamed. She weeps.

A children's party comes in dancing a Polonaise.
Polonaise tempo
f
She tries to join them but
is constantly pushed out.
2

Polka tempo
f
7
mf
f

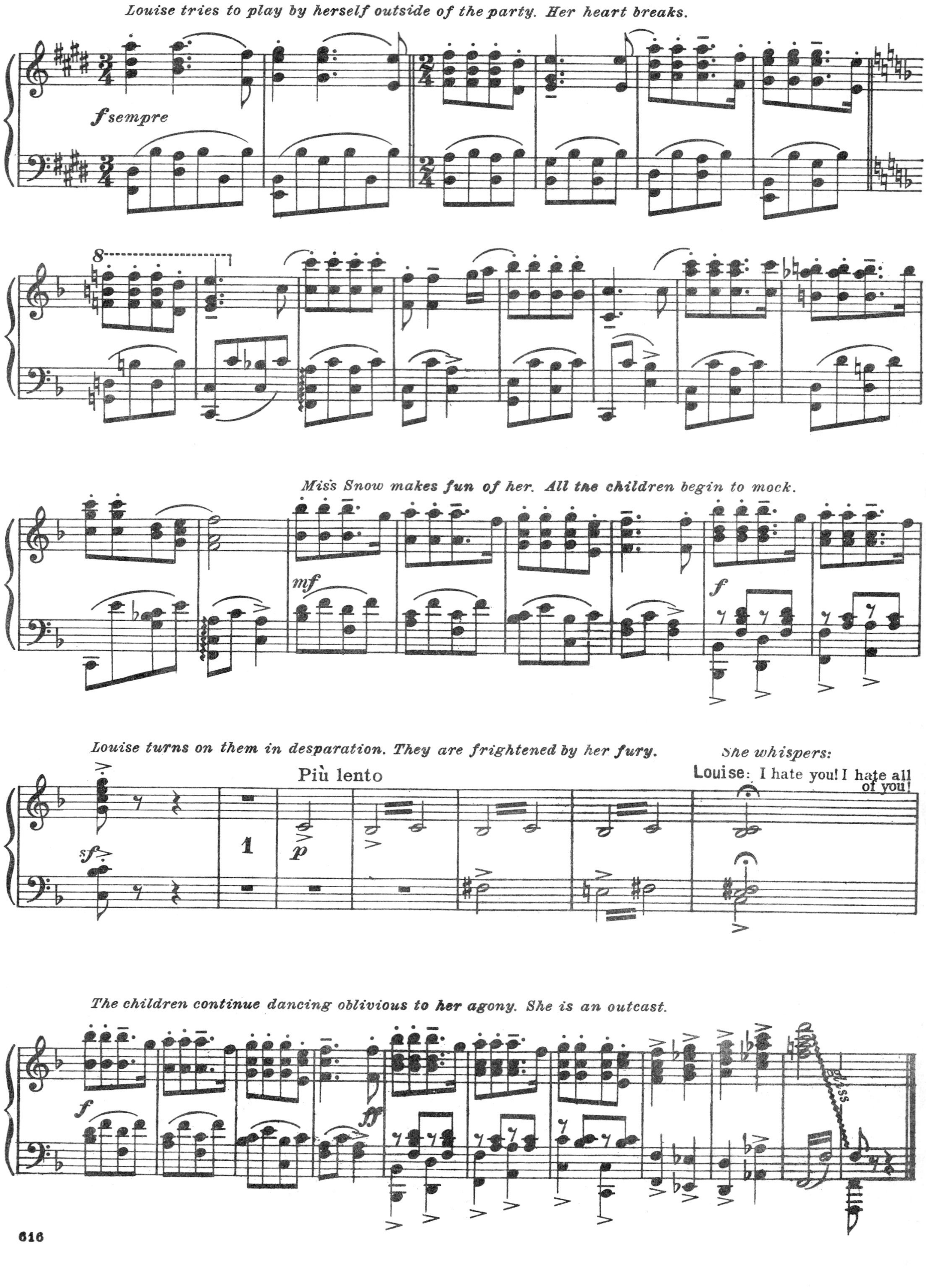

Louise tries to play by herself outside of the party. Her heart breaks.
f sempre
8
Miss Snow makes fun of her. All the children begin to mock.
mf
f
Louise turns on them in desparation. They are frightened by her fury.
She whispers:
Più lento
Louise: I hate you! I hate all of you!
sf
1
p
The children continue dancing oblivious to her agony. She is an outcast.
f
ff
gliss

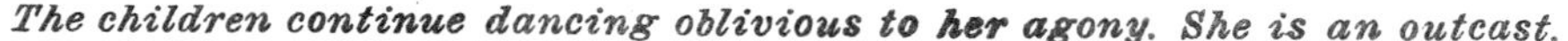

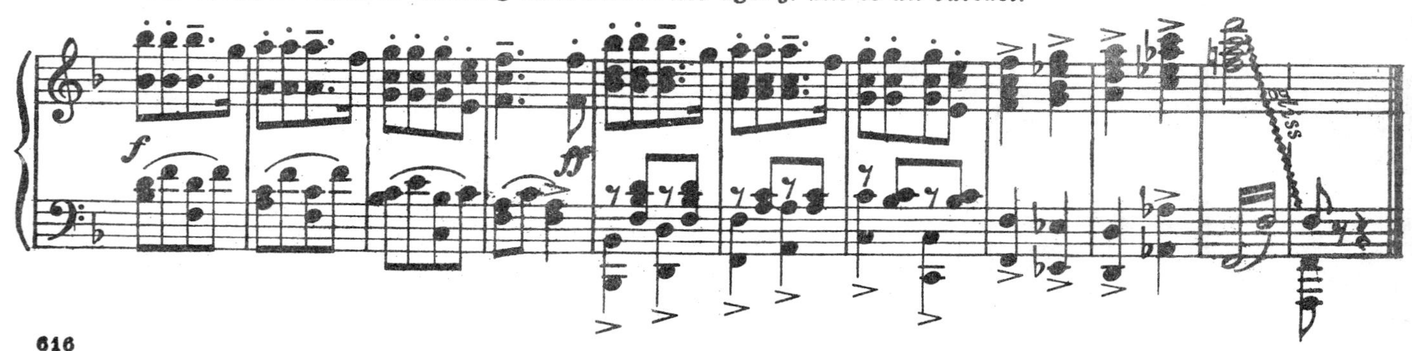

"My little girl" (Reprise)

No. 28

Cue: After Ballet, Billy and Starkeeper enter.

Starkeeper: (Heavenly Friend appears)
Ay-eh, somebody ought to. You can go down town anytime. Offer's still open.

Billy steals a star. Then whistling walks off with Heavenly Friend.

Curtain opens on Porch Scene

Carrie's incidental

No. 29

Cue: Julie: That's a good girl. Run along.
Carrie: She threw her leg over a fence like this___

(Carrie sings unaccompanied)

Allegretto
I'm a Tom - boy, jest a Tom - boy! I'm a

mad - cap maid - en from Broad - way! I'm a Tom - boy,___ a mer - ry

(Mr. Snow enters with Snow Jr. and interrupts song.)
Tom - boy, I'm a mad - cap maid - en from Broad - way!___

Porch Scene

(Act II, Scene 5)

No. 30

Cue: Julie: *(coming out)* Where is he?

Julie:
Go into the house, child!
Louise:
What happened, Mother? Don't you believe me?
Julie:
Yes, I believe you.
Louise:
Then why don't you tell me why you're actin' so funny?
Julie:
It's nothin', darling.
allargando
Louise:
But is it possible fer someone to hit you hard like that–real loud and hard–and not hurt you at all?
Julie:
It is possible, dear, fer someone to hit you–hit you hard–and not hurt at all.
(Louise embraces her mother and runs into the house. Julie sees star, walks to chair, picks it up.)
Appassionato
a tempo f

Billy: (speaks) Julie! Julie!
Billy: (sings)
Long - ing to tell you but a - fraid and shy,
mf
Billy:
I let my gold - en chanc - es pass me by.
Billy:
Now I've lost you, Soon I will go in the mist of day,
3
3

Billy:
And you nev - er will know,
cresc.
How I loved you, How I loved you.
f
p
8
pp
(The curtain of stars falls, leaving Billy and Heavenly Friend in front)
Billy:
She took the star, she took it! Seems like she knew I was there.
ⓑ Passionately
f
3
3
p
Heavenly Friend:
Julie would always know.
Billy:
She never changes.
Heavenly Friend:
No, Julie, never changes.

Billy: But my little girl, my Louise–
I gotta do somethin' for her.
Heavenly Friend:
So far you haven't done much.
Moderato
p dolce
Billy:
I know, I know.
Heavenly Friend:
Time's running out.
Billy: But it ain't over yet. I want an ex-
tension. I gotta see that graduation.
Heavenly Friend:
All right Billy! (They exit)
(Music increases for change of scenery to Gra-
cresc.
duation Scene. Cut ff music abruptly, when change ready.)
f

Graduation Scene

(Finale Ultimo)

No. 31

Cue: Doctor: Maybe you still sing it—

Moderato

Doctor: "When you walk through a storm, keep your chin up high." Know that one?

Piano
pp

Girls:
pp
And don't be a - fraid of the
pp

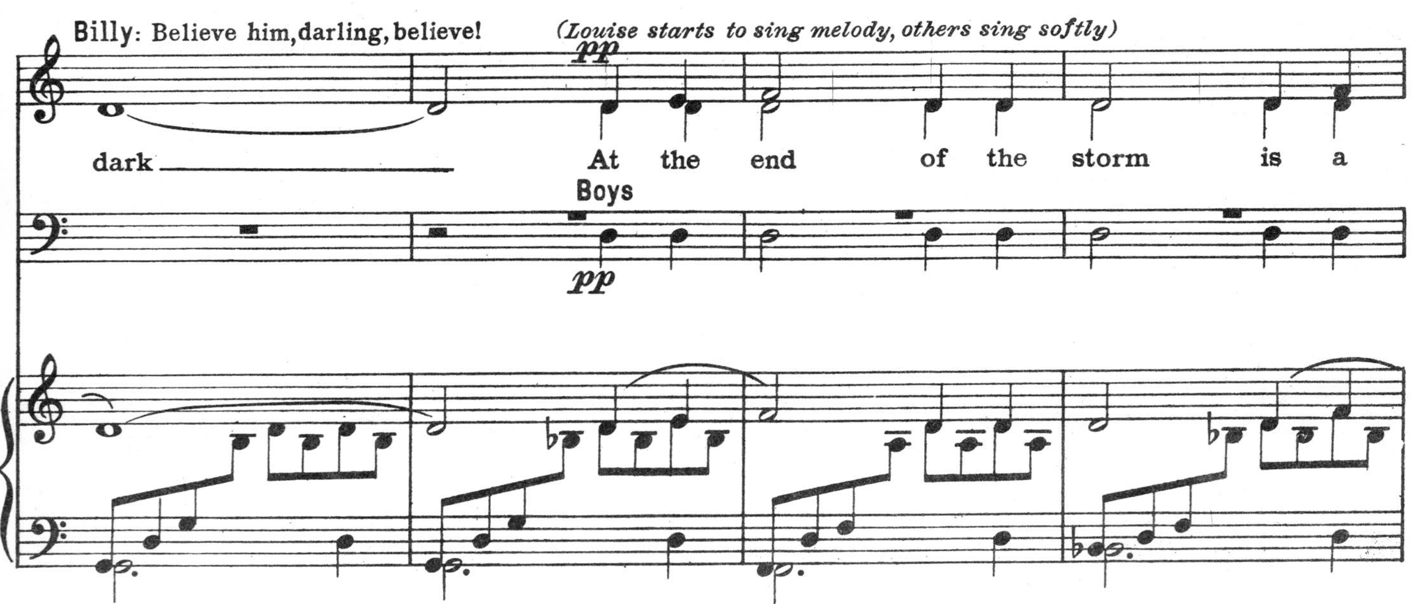
Billy: Believe him, darling, believe!
(Louise starts to sing melody, others sing softly)
pp
dark
At the end of the storm is a
Boys
pp

Girls:
gold - en sky And the sweet silv - er song of the lark.
Boys:
rall.
mf
Walk on through the wind, walk on through the rain though your
mf
a tempo
mf
Billy: (to Julie)
I loved you, Julie,
know that I loved you.
Julie: (starts singing)
p cresc. poco a poco
pp
dreams be tossed and blown. Walk on, walk
pp
p cresc. poco a poco
dim.
pp
p cresc.
poco a poco

(The singing becomes exalted)
Girls:
on with hope in your heart And you'll nev - er
Boys:
f sempre cresc.
walk a - lone, You'll nev - er walk a -
ff
with great expression
Maestoso
Final curtain
lone.
ff
sff
8